Bond

No.1 for exam success

C000193444

English and **Verbal** Reasoning

Assessment Papers

CEM
(Durham University)

9–10 years

OXFORD

UNIVERSITY PRESS

OXFORD
UNIVERSITY PRESS

Great Clarendon Street, Oxford, OX2 6DP, United Kingdom

Oxford University Press is a department of the University of Oxford.
It furthers the University's objective of excellence in research, scholarship,
and education by publishing worldwide. Oxford is a registered trade mark of
Oxford University Press in the UK and in certain other countries

British Library Cataloguing in Publication Data
Data available

978-0-19-274283-4

10 9 8 7

Paper used in the production of this book is a natural, recyclable product
made from wood grown in sustainable forests. The manufacturing process
conforms to the environmental regulations of the country of origin.

Printed in Great Britain by Ashford Colour Press Ltd.

Acknowledgements
Page make-up: Tech-Set Ltd, Gateshead
Illustrations: Beehive Illustration
Cover illustrations: Lo Cole

Before you get started

What is Bond?

This book is part of the Bond CEM Assessment Papers series for English and Verbal Reasoning, which provides **thorough and continuous practice of key English and Verbal Reasoning skills** from ages eight to eleven. Bond's resources are ideal preparation for Key Stage 1 and Key Stage 2 SATs, the 11[+], the CEE and other selective school entrance exams.

How does the scope of this book match real exam content?

Each paper is carefully pitched to ensure a smooth progression towards the next level. Unlike other 11[+] papers, the CEM exam is a combination of literacy **and** verbal reasoning questions. They cover comprehension, vocabulary, spellings, grammar and logical reasoning, with a higher emphasis on word knowledge. The question format is much more varied and this holistic approach to learning key skills, rather than learning question styles, will also provide a rigorous foundation for other exams.

The coverage of grammar, vocabulary, comprehension and spellings is matched to the National Curriculum and the National Literacy Strategy and will also **provide invaluable preparation for Key Stage 2 SATs**. The aim of the CEM exam is to constantly change the style and format of questions. This makes it outside of the scope of any book to provide a prescriptive series of papers, but the Bond CEM papers are based on the range and styles of questions asked in previous exams alongside a solid foundation of the **key skills that will underpin the CEM exams**.

Some schools may also include a written composition as part of the 11[+] exam. Although it is outside the scope of this book to practise extended and creative writing skills, *Bond Focus on Writing* provides full coverage of writing skills.

What does the book contain?

- **6 papers** – each one contains 75 questions.
- **Tutorial links throughout** – 📖 – this icon appears in the margin next to the questions. It indicates links to the relevant section in *How To Do CEM English and Verbal Reasoning*, our invaluable subject guide that offers explanations and practice for all core question types.
- **Scoring devices** – there are score boxes in the margins and a Progress Chart on page 68. The chart is a visual and motivating way for children to see how they are doing. It also turns the score into a percentage that can help inform what to do next.
- **Answers** – located in an easily-removed central pull-out section.

How can you use this book?

One of the great strengths of Bond Assessment Papers is their flexibility. They can be used at home, in school and by tutors to:

- set **timed formal practice** tests – allow about 45 minutes per paper in line with standard 11+ demands. Gradually reduce the suggested time limit by ten minutes to practise working at speed
- provide **bite-sized chunks** for regular practice
- highlight **strengths and weaknesses** in the core skills
- identify **individual needs**
- set **homework**
- follow **a complete 11+ preparation strategy** alongside *The Parents' Guide to the 11+* (see below).

It is best to start at the beginning and work through the papers in order to make the best use of the Progress Chart. If you are using the book as part of a careful run-in to the 11+, we suggest that you also have four other essential Bond resources close at hand:

- *How To Do CEM English and Verbal Reasoning*: the subject guide that explains all the question types practised in this book. Use the cross-reference icons to find the relevant sections.

- *Focus on Comprehension*: the practical handbook that clearly shows children how to read and understand the text, understand the questions and assess their own answers.

- *Focus on Writing*: the essential resource that explains the key components of successful writing.

- *The Parents' Guide to the 11+*: the step-by-step guide to the whole 11+ experience. It clearly explains the 11+ process, provides guidance on how to assess children, helps you to set complete action plans for practice and explains how you can use *CEM English and Verbal Reasoning 9-10 Assessment Papers* as part of a strategic run-in to the exam.

What does a score mean and how can it be improved?

It is unfortunately impossible to guarantee that a child will pass the 11+ exam if they achieve a certain score on any practice book or paper. Success on the day depends on a host of factors, including the scores of the other children sitting the test. However, we can provide invaluable guidance on what a score indicates and how to improve it.

If children colour in the Progress Chart on page 68, this will give an idea of present performance in percentage terms. The Next Steps Planner inside the back cover will help you to decide what to do next to help a child progress.

It is always valuable to go over wrong answers with children. If they are having trouble with any particular question type, follow the tutorial links to *How To Do CEM English and Verbal Reasoning* for step-by-step explanations and further practice. Bond offers the complete range of resources for you and your child, to give you the maximum support that you need.

Don't forget the website …!

Visit www.bond11plus.co.uk for lots of advice, information and suggestions on everything to do with Bond, the 11+ and helping children to achieve their best.

Key words

Some special words are used in this book. You will find them in **bold** each time they appear in the Papers. These words are explained here.

abstract noun   a word referring to a concept or idea, for example *imagination*

adjective   a word that describes someone or something

adverb   a word that describes an action

alliteration   a repetition of the same sound, for example *five funny frogs*

antonym   a word with a meaning opposite to another word, for example *wet – dry*

conjunction   a word that links sentences, phrases or words, for example *and, because*

noun   a word for somebody or something

onomatopoeic   a word that echoes a sound associated with its meaning, for example *snap*

past tense   a verb that has already happened

phrase   a group of words that act as a unit

plural   more than one of something, for example *men*

preposition   a word that describes where a noun is, for example *on, under, with*

pronoun   a word that replaces a noun, for example *him, her, it, they*

proper noun   the name of a person, place, date or day, for example *Marion, April, Friday*

root word   a word which can have a prefix/suffix added to it, for example *unfriendly*

sentence   a group of words that makes sense standing alone

simile   an expression that describes something as being like something else, for example *the sun was as round as a golden coin*

suffix   a group of letters added to the end of a word, for example *fully, ed, ing*

superfluous   an additional word that is not needed in a sentence, as the sentence works perfectly well without it, for example *the handsome man drove the car home*

synonym   a word with a meaning similar to another word, for example *smile, grin*

verb   an action or doing word

Read the following comprehension text and answer the questions that follow it.

The Magpie by Claude Monet

Claude Monet was born in France on the 14th November 1840. In the winter of
1868–69, Monet began his work on *The Magpie*, a well-known snowscape. In this
painting, there is a house behind trees with a fence in the foreground. A gate is in
5 the fence and a magpie sits upon the top. The little magpie becomes the focus of
the painting. The scene is snowy, with a white sky leading down to the white fields
with more trees covered in snow. Although snow is cold and barren, it also covers
sharp corners, creating a blanketing effect. The stone of the building has a warm
pinkish flesh tone which is picked up in the sky, the fence and the tree trunks.
10 This shows the real beauty of light. The shadows from the fence and gate are
blue-tinged, which balances the pink and is very different to the work of previous
artists who would have painted shadows in black or grey. Another revolutionary
technique that Monet uses is short brush strokes, which allows him to control
the lighting effect and gives a real feeling of movement, a crucial technique that
15 challenges previous ways of painting.

Monet wanted his paintings to reflect the changes that light has on nature.
This meant that he spent hours outside watching and experiencing these changes
of light. By remaining in the same place and simply watching, Monet learnt from
nature, rather than from previous artists. Where we might consider a snowscape
20 to be white, there is actually very little, if any, pure white. Monet layers tinted white
upon tinted white to show distance, depth of snow and the length of shadows.
It is said that Monet wanted to avoid painting things, but that he wanted to paint
the air that surrounded things. It gives this painting the look of having been lit from
underneath and is both realistic and beautiful. What is so surprising to us today is
25 that the art world of the time did not take to Monet's lightness of touch and palette
of pale colours. It rejected his painting.

Monet painted 140 snowscapes with the first one, *A Cart on the Snowy Road at Hornfleur*, painted less than five years previously, but *The Magpie* is the largest of Monet's snowscapes. This painting is so important as it shows the natural

30   effects of snow, a new way of considering the colour of shadows, and this effect becomes associated with a major movement within art: Impressionism. If you haven't yet seen this beautiful work of art, the original can be found the Musee d'Orsay in Paris. Until then, it can be looked up online and enjoyed.

1 How old was Monet when he started painting *The Magpie*? _____

2 Which four of the following statements are false? Tick the correct boxes.

   a There is a magpie sitting upon a gate. ☐

   b There is a stone building in the picture. ☐

   c Monet has carefully controlled his black painted shadows. ☐

   d Monet uses long sweeps of his paintbrush. ☐

   e Monet spent time outside watching how the light changes. ☐

   f Monet has used a lot of pure white in the painting. ☐

   g Monet was born in Belgium. ☐

3 What do these words mean as used in the text?

   a focus (line 5)

   _____

   b tinged (line 11)

   _____

   c revolutionary (line 12)

   _____

4 Why does the snow have a 'blanketing effect' (line 8)?

_____

_____

_____

5 In what three ways is *The Magpie* a significant painting?

_____

_____

_____

6 The word 'mean' has become 'meant'. This is because the spelling rule changes the word in the **past tense** so instead of 'mean' becoming 'meaned' we use the 't' instead to make 'meant'. Can you find another word in the text that also follows this spelling rule?

1 E

1

_____

Complete each **sentence** by selecting the best word from the options **a, b, c, d** or **e**.

8 mins

3 E

Example   People travelling to certain countries need _____ *d – vaccination* _____ .

a	b	c	d	e
immunity	certainty	vacation	vaccination	respiration

7 Which _____ does this book fit into as it isn't really poetry?

a	b	c	d	e
size	author	category	group	colour

8 I felt so _____ to be spotted in town when I was supposed to be off sick.

a	b	c	d	e
awkward	pleased	proud	jealous	touched

9 I cannot _____ between pizza or pasta.

a	b	c	d	e
guess	option	decide	choice	prefer

10 We saw _____ types of fish at the fish market.

a	b	c	d	e
kind	nice	variety	vary	various

4

Rearrange these words to make the longest **sentence** you can. Underline the word that is **superfluous**.

1 H

Example   So cream <u>eat</u> the were cakes delicious.
                The cream cakes were so delicious.

11 Circus artists there are in a trapeze agile.

_____

12 Defender from football the escaped the manager.

_____

13 Police prison time spend a of people convicted crime might in a.

_____

14 Homemade chef is cheap nutritious meal and a soup.

_____

Find the three letters that complete these words. The three letters do not have to make a word.

Example   fr**es**h spl**as**h

15 addr_____ es   l_____racy

16 mater_____ s   ap_____rs

17 bicy_____   yach_____g

18 spe_____l   b_____the

19 cert_____ly   bla_____n

20 hei_____en   consi_____ate

Read the following **sentences** and answer the questions.

Example   'The plane's departure time was 13:45.'
         What does the word 'departure' mean? Answer: **b**

a	**b**	**c**	**d**
arriving	<u>leaving</u>	resting	mending

21 'Is there enough custard in that jug for all of us?'
    What does the word 'enough' mean?

a	**b**	**c**	**d**
lots	plenty	deficient	sufficient

22 'We followed our guide as he took us around the gallery.'
    What does the word 'guide' mean?

a	**b**	**c**	**d**
server	management	light	escort

23 'I knew it was disastrous when the downpour hit our tent.'
What does the word 'disastrous' means?

a	b	c	d
dreadful	positive	funny	scary

24 'Out of curiosity, I took a peek through the fence to see the neighbours' new dog.'
What does the word 'curiosity' mean?

a	b	c	d
pride	humour	sadness	nosiness

25 'There was an air of nervousness as the pupils sat down in silence.'
What does the word 'nervousness' mean?

a	b	c	d
pleasure	fun	anxiety	annoyance

5

Underline the two odd words out in the following groups of words.

16 mins

2 F

Example   purple   lilac   <u>olive</u>   <u>sage</u>   violet

26 head   neck   toe   heel   sole

27 kitten   puppy   calf   horse   donkey

28 bowl   lunch   dish   breakfast   supper

29 candy   sweet   sour   bitter   cream

30 hat   blouse   scarf   trousers   gloves

31 hide   reveal   open   conceal   expose

6

Write the **plural** version of the words in these **sentences**.

4 A

Example   The hairdresser owned a selection of <u>brushes</u>. (brush)

32 When we went on holiday last summer, we saw a campsite with lots of

_____ (caravan) on it.

33 The site had a toilet block, a shower block and a few _____
(shop), and it was well geared up for families.

34 There were woodland nature _____ (walk) to do, with lots of trees, plants and things to look at.

35 For anyone that felt unable to complete long walks, there were plenty of

_____ (bench) to sit down and rest.

36 At the other side of the site were some _____ (swing), slides and climbing frames for boys and girls to play on.

37 That impressive restaurant is called the _____ (chimney) and you certainly wouldn't miss the building!

38 They hold many _____ (party) for special occasions, from weddings and anniversaries to Christmas dos.

39 For _____ (child) there is a special area called the jungle room, which is an amazing place to play.

40 It is decorated with elephants and _____ (monkey), giraffes and an amazing selection of colourful birds.

41 Snakes slither on the ground and baboon _____ (baby) dangle off tree branches.

○ 10

3 D

Underline the correct words in each of these **sentences**.

Example   She (<u>blew</u>, blue) her trumpet solo in the school (<u>band</u>, banned).

42 I learnt a sad (lessen, lesson) when I (threw, through) a stone at the greenhouse window.

43 The farmer had to (sew, sow) the seeds in (rose, rows) across the patchwork of fields.

44 The double egg (yoke, yolk) was a fascinating (sight, site).

45 We have just one (hour, our) to go shopping in the (sails, sales) and we have a lot of things to look at.

○ 4

Look at the following words and then use them to answer the questions that follow.

savage	package	remind	missing	notice
behaviour	proper	conduct	voyage	absent
silent	manage	postage	respond	performance
repent	record	police	report	import
brutal	away	cope	mute	survive

46 Find two words that are **synonyms** for the word 'fierce'.

_____

47 Find three words that are **antonyms** for the word 'present'.

_____

_____

2 B

48 Find three words that are **synonyms** for the word 'manner'.

_____

_____

2 A

49 Find three words that are **antonyms** for the word 'fail'.

_____

_____

2 B

50 Find two words that are **synonyms** for the word 'quiet'.

_____

2 A

13

Underline the one word on the right that has the most similar meaning to the word on the left.

2 C

Example   vision   plotting / smell / <u>sight</u> / style / map

51 clumsy   awkward / falling / ill / foolish / clumping

52 lose   baggy / slack / mislay / win / result

53 holy   church / sacred / priest / religion / mesh

54 flood   plague / babble / trickle / poor / torrent

55 else   and / because / but / otherwise / hence

56 disgust   revulsion / disguise / windy / nasty / dread

57 fortune   money / payment / extreme / destiny / tarot

7

Take a different **conjunction** from the box and place it in a space so that each **sentence** makes sense.

but	and	provided	or	which

58 I wanted to play out _____ Mum said that I had to come in as it was getting far too late.

59 They drove towards town, _____ was the wrong direction for getting to the birthday party.

60 You can have some fruit _____ you eat your vegetables.

61 You can either choose the toffees _____ the fudge.

62 I'm pleased with your results _____ even more thrilled by your effort.

Find the three-letter word that can be added to the letters in capitals to make a new word. The new word will complete the **sentence** sensibly.

Example   We HED the keys to the estate agent. <u>AND</u>

63 Mum and Dad drove to the seaside without booking a room in advance, but fortunately the hotel had VACIES for that week. _____

64 The sailors began their VOY around Africa, which was going to be an incredibly long journey. _____

65 I ICKED when I saw the huge spider climbing across the ceiling and down the wall towards me. _____

66 The STALLIZED fruit decorated the top of the cake, making it the centrepiece of the buffet table. _____

67 The minimal cake was SIM decorated with a single rose, which complemented the delicate rose-flavoured sponge. _____

68–75 The following paragraph has nine incorrectly spelled words. Underline the misspelled words and write the correct spellings in the right-hand box. The first one has been done for you.

When Mr Hoskins <u>retyred</u> he didn't know what he was going to do with himself. He didn't have many hobys other than cicleing and ocasionnal gardening. He went to the local libery to see if he could find any books that would intrest him and then he found it! A book about heros in history cort his fancy and reading about the bravry that people had shown was inspiring.	Eg. Retired
	68
	69
	70
	71
	72
	73
	74
	75

8

Now go to the Progress Chart to record your score!   Total   90

Paper 2

Add the missing letters to the word on the right to make a word with the opposite meaning to the word on the left.

Example   ascended   d _e_ _s_ c _e_ nd _e_ _d_

1 rigid   fl __ __ i __ le

2 male   __ e __ a __ __

3 advance   r __ t __ e __ t

4 major   m __ __ o __

5 start   __ __ __ __ sh

6 birth   d __ __ __ h

6

Complete each **sentence** by selecting the best word from the options **a**, **b**, **c**, **d** or **e**.

Example   People travelling to certain countries need _____**d – vaccination**_____ .

a	b	c	d	e
immunity	certainty	vacation	vaccination	respiration

7 I enjoy netball and a range of crafts in my _____ time.

a	b	c	d	e
leisure	cheap	relax	hobbies	extra

8 That monkey has a _____ way of swinging upside down.

a	b	c	d	e
common	regular	odd	peculiar	ugly

9 Is it _____ for you to finish your lesson early this afternoon?

a	b	c	d	e
probable	certainty	unlikely	possible	likely

10 That dog is so _____ ; he has stolen the pie from the basket.

a	b	c	d	e
argumentative	mischievous	boring	good	rascal

4

Underline the one word on the right that has the most similar meaning to the word on the left.

Example   vision   plotting / smell / <u>sight</u> / style / map

11 portray   receive / send / represent / disclose / interest

12 reply   respond / ask / request / command / order

13 excuse   manners / polite / justice / justify / rudeness

14 scare   worry / frighten / annoy / entertain / bore

15 exchange   altered / swap / turn / rotate / lend

16 strength   light / agility / power / heavy / ornate

17 except   include / exclude / overdue / other / instead

2 C

7

Underline the two odd words out in the following groups of words.

2 F

Example   purple   lilac   <u>olive</u>   <u>sage</u>   violet

18 lake	park	river	fields	brook
19 nest	bungalow	den	house	cottage
20 pear	apple	lemon	orange	grapefruit
21 guard	pillow	protect	shelter	duvet
22 fog	snow	frost	winter	weather

5

Write the **plural** version of the words in these **sentences**.

13 mins

4 A

Example   Where are the <u>cats</u>? (cat)

23 Every morning the _____ (worker) set off to work.

24 The _____ (bus) picked up people from all over the area.

25 They dropped people off at _____ (factory) on the estate.

26 Most of the work involved making and packaging _____ (match).

17

27 Then _____ (box) had to be loaded into the parking bays.

28 Now they are ready for the _____ (lorry) to deliver them to the shops.

6

Find the three-letter word that can be added to the capital letters to make a new word. The new word will complete the **sentence** sensibly.

A

Example   We HED the keys to the estate agent.   <u>AND</u>

29 The department store had a CLANCE sale in the toy section, which was very exciting news for lots of boys and girls. _____

30 The whole school stayed in log CAS during their week away at the nature reservation. _____

31 'It is FIDDEN to run along school corridors', the head teacher said in morning assembly. _____

32 My flower basket had TRING ivy that hung down beautifully. _____

33 When I was unwell I needed IBIOTIC medicine to get better. _____

34 The portrait was an OINAL by a famous artist and yet it hung in the charity shop for very little money. _____

35 The little boy loved to eat ketchup with his VEABLES, but as long as he was eating, his mum was happy. _____

7

Rearrange these words to make the longest **sentence** you can.
Underline the word that is **superfluous**.

H

Example   So cream <u>eat</u> the were cakes delicious.
The cream cakes were so delicious.

36 Buddy all paired infant lunch are children school up with a.

_____

37 Pupils on sit to beanbags our library with quiet area a has reading.

_____

18

38 Had Michael a tired was so he a lie-down.

_____

39 Snowed fun it sledging when to go friends loved and her Jawahir.

_____

40 Time their volleyball play chose the boys to beach in free dear.

_____

5

3 G

Read the following **sentences** and answer the questions.

Example   'The plane's departure time was 13:45.'
            What does the word 'departure' mean? Answer: **b**

a	b	c	d
arriving	<u>leaving</u>	resting	mending

'There has been a recent change in the law regarding dangerous dogs.'

41 i What does the word 'recent' mean?

a	b	c	d
currant	latest	obvious	difficult

ii What does the word 'regarding' mean?

a	b	c	d
concerning	viewing	purposing	despite

'We placed our precious possessions into the trunk for safekeeping.'

42 i What does the word 'precious' mean?

a	b	c	d
pretty	unique	treasured	worship

ii What does the word 'trunk' mean?

a	b	c	d
elephant	nose	envelope	case

2

Take a different **conjunction** from the box and place it in a space so that each **sentence** makes sense.

after	*although*	*as*	*but*	*when*

43 Raoul cannot attend on Monday _____ he has a dentist's appointment and will not be back in time.

44 _____ it is my party, I will still have time to help out in the restaurant if you would like me to.

45 Aswan can go out to play _____ he has eaten his supper.

46 _____ I have marked the books, you will all get your results, so working quietly now will allow me to get on with the marking.

47 At the weekend I received my birthday present, I wrote a letter to grandma

_____ I haven't posted it yet.

5

Underline the correct words in each of these **sentences**.

3 D

Example   She (<u>blew</u>, blue) her trumpet solo in the school (<u>band</u>, banned).

48 We can grind (cereal, serial) into (flour, flower) that we can use to bake bread and cakes.

49 I tried to (die, dye) my (hair, hare) bright purple for fundraising day but it has taken so long to wash out.

50 I have a blister on my (heal, heel) and another on the (sole, soul) of my foot because we walked so far.

51 I wanted to (buy, bye) a (currant, current) bun from the baker's but they had sold out.

52 (Weather, whether) we go camping or not depends upon the (weather, whether).

53 (Their, they're) still playing at the park, but (it's, its) nearly bedtime so I will go and fetch them.

54 The (waives, waves) on the sea today look really (rough, ruff) so I am glad that I am not on a fishing trawler.

7

20

Read the following passage and then find two examples of each word class to complete the table below.

The hawk sat powerfully on the treetop thoroughly surveying the ground below until his piercing eyes spotted a movement in the tall grass. A grey mouse wouldn't feed a hungry hawk, but it would make a tasty snack.

55	noun		
56	verb		
57	pronoun		
58	adjective		
59	adverb		
60	preposition		
61	conjunction		

7

62–67 Some of the words in this paragraph have letters missing. Write out the complete words in the right-hand box, so that the spellings are correct and the paragraph makes sense. The first word has been done for you.

Emily's g __ __ __ __ a, who was called Fudge, was p __ __ __ ly. He wasn't eating properly and Emily was worried. Her mum took Fudge to the vet. The vet said that the little ani __ __ __ had an inf __ __ __ ion and wrote out a prescri __ __ __ __ __ for some antibiotics. Five days later and Fudge was running around again back to perfect h __ __ __ __ h. Emily was now much hap __ __ __ __.	Eg. guinea
	62
	63
	64
	65
	66
	67

6

Twills Theme Park for the Best Ever Thrills...

DARE TO RIDE ON THE BONE SHAKER?

A slow climb upwards followed by the rickety road downwards to the darkest pit.

Only the bravest survive this white knuckle ride...

FANCY THE SHARK SURVIVOR?

A vertigo adventure of 15 loops as you swing and dangle above the shark infested waters before being lowered into the water below.

Only the fish will hear you scream...

EXPERIENCE THE THRILL OF THE DROP OF DEATH...

Steeper, deeper, taller, faster, crazier – that is one awesome ride. Plunge at 70mph down the 400 foot drop before being thrown backwards.

We dare you to do the Drop of Death...

MASSIVE 25% OFF WITH THIS FLYER!

Plus many more rides, restaurants and cafes, shops, ride photography, gifts, amusement arcades, baby Twills Fun Fair and petting farm for little Twillers, 280 acres of Shropshire countryside to enjoy with walks, nature trails, and boat trips on the lake. Disabled access, plenty of seating areas, free activities.

- Print tickets online to save up to 20%
- Special VIP tickets to jump the queues
- Huge free car park for over 2000 cars and 200 coaches
- Theme park open 365 days a year from 10:00 am – 10:00 pm

www.twillsthemepark.co.uk   05432 101 1001

AN AMAZING DAY OUT FOR ALL OF THE FAMILY. COME TO TWILLS FOR ENDLESS EXCITEMENT, THRILLS AND SPILLS.

68 What three rides are mentioned in the text?

_____

_____

_____

69 What county is Twills in?

_____

70 Find eight words or short **phrases** that are used in the flyer to make the theme park seem exciting.

_____

_____

_____

_____

71 What do these words mean as used in the text?

  a rickety

_____

  b awesome

_____

  c plunge

_____

72 If Arthur was five years old, would Twills be suitable for him? Find three pieces of information from the text to support your answer.

_____

_____

_____

_____

_____

73 Arthur's great-grandfather dislikes too much noise and his great-grandmother is in a wheelchair. Would Twills be suitable for them? Find three pieces of information from the text to support your answer.

1 B

_____

_____

_____

_____

_____

4

74 What benefits would there be if we printed out some VIP tickets online and then took the tickets and this flyer with us to Twills?

1 B

_____

_____

_____

_____

2

75 The word 'steep' has the **suffix** 'er' added to it. Can you find another two words in this same paragraph that have the same spelling rule?

1 E

_____

2

Now go to the Progress Chart to record your score!   Total   90

Paper 3

The underlined words in this paragraph have not been spelled correctly. Write out the misspelled words in the right-hand box, so that the spellings are correct and the paragraph makes sense. The first word has been done for you.

The Vikings built difrent types of ships. For rayding countries they had their fearsly decorated longships. For fishing they had compacked boats and they projuiced cargo ships called knorrs. The longship could sail in open seas and in shalo water so that they could sail right up a river to spring a suprise attack and then make a quick retreet.	Eg. different 1 2 3 4 5 6 7

7

Look at the following words and then use them to answer the questions that follow.

forty	damage	property	parent	consist
advantage	wages	serpent	prevent	silence
remarkable	blanket	stretch	former	also
furnish	organ	almost	curtain	orchard
prohibit	expand	digital	thermal	purple

8 Find two words that are **synonyms** for the word 'spread'.

_____

9 Find two words that are **antonyms** for the word 'allow'.

_____

10 Find one word that is a **synonym** for the word 'benefit'.

_____

11 Find one word that is an **antonym** for the word 'noise'.

_____

12 Find one word that is a **synonym** for the word 'nearly'.

2 A

_____

13 Find one word that is an **antonym** for the word 'repair'.

2 B

_____

14 Find one word that is a **synonym** for the word 'snake'.

2 A

_____

9

Underline the one word on the right that has the most similar meaning to the word on the left.

2 C

Example   vision   plotting / smell / <u>sight</u> / style / map

15 several   some / few / many / seldom / frequent

16 local   shop / supermarket / far / abroad / regional

17 idea   perfect / thought / thinking / feeling / imagination

18 choke   strangle / force / throat / neck / swallow

19 owe   money / payments / poverty / lend / indebted

5

Rearrange these words to make the longest **sentence** you can.
Underline the word that is **superfluous**.

10 mins

3 H

Example: So cream <u>eat</u> the were cakes delicious.
                The cream cakes were so delicious.

20 Mirror was that tidy in my hair the I checked at.

_____

21 His computer plug needed to recharge my dad laptop.

_____

22 Arabella a tiny cage her hamsters tiger pet for bigger wanted.

_____

23 Environment out protecting about the learnt we today assembly in.

_____

4

Take a different **conjunction** from the box and place it in a space so that each **sentence** makes sense.

unless	*whenever*	*if*	*but*	*when*	*although*

24 We visit the local market _____ we go to our caravan as it is so exciting to see how the local people shop.

25 The freedom to speak is so important _____ inciting hatred is horrible, especially when it leads to unrest.

26 She won't get into the team _____ she puts in the hard work, and I don't think that she has thought about this

27 _____ we have made popcorn for years, we have only just made these flavours.

28 I'll mow the back lawn _____ the weather is dry enough as I managed to mow the front lawn last week.

29 _____ I miss that train I shall be annoyed.

Find the three letters that complete these words. The three letters do not have to make a word.

Example   fr<u>esh</u>   spl<u>ash</u>

30 suppo_____ g   t_____ efore

31 th_____ ht   vari_____ ly

32 w_____ hty   reme_____ r

33 separ_____   c_____ oard

34 stren_____   ans_____ ing

35 isl_____ s   le_____ h

Add the missing letters to the word on the right to make a word with the opposite meaning to the word on the left.

Example   ascended   d <u>e</u> <u>s</u> c <u>e</u> nd <u>e</u> <u>d</u>

36 entertaining   b __ r __ n __

37 freedom   s __ __ __ __ r y

38 result   c a __ __ __

39 friendly   __ o __ t __ l __

40 obey   i __ n __ r e

Look at the following tanks in the Waterworld Fish Aquarium. Which fish are where?

Tank A   Tank B   Tank C   Tank D

Tank E   Tank F   Tank G   Tank H

The sharks and fighting fish are at the end of a row. The goldfish are between the fighting fish and the minnows and are below the angelfish. The weather loaches are in a tank above the guppies and are next to the tetras, who are next to the angelfish. The sharks are left of the angel fish.

41 Tank A = _____   Tank B = _____

     Tank C = _____   Tank D = _____

42 Tank E = _____   Tank F = _____

     Tank G = _____   Tank H = _____

Underline the correct words in each of these **sentences**.

Example   She (<u>blew</u>, blue) her trumpet solo in the school (<u>band</u>, banned).

43 To (waist, waste) water is not the (right, write) thing to do as we shold look after our natural resources.

44 I would love a (peace, piece) of chocolate cake for my (super, supper) as Mum has been baking all afternoon.

45 A successful business makes a financial (profit, prophet) each year (which, witch) is a reassuring sign for their shareholders.

46 Our school computer (suite, sweet) is on the second floor and also houses the (stationary, stationery) cupboard.

4

Read the following **sentences** and answer the questions.

Example   'The plane's departure time was 13:45.'
What does the word 'departure' mean? Answer: **b**

a	**b**	**c**	**d**
arriving	<u>leaving</u>	resting	mending

47 'There was sufficient evidence to convict the man who harassed us.'

i What does the word 'sufficient' mean?

a	**b**	**c**	**d**
adequate	weak	inflexible	provable

ii What does the word 'harassed' mean?

a	**b**	**c**	**d**
entertained	abandoned	pestered	ignored

48 'It is necessary to vacate this shop so please leave the store immediately.'

i What does the word 'vacate' mean?

a	**b**	**c**	**d**
clean	empty	vaccinate	open

ii What does the word 'immediately' mean?

a	**b**	**c**	**d**
later	sometime	instantly	whenever

49 'There will be an opportunity for you to persuade us with your ideas.'

   i What does the word 'opportunity' mean?

a	b	c	d
occasion	eventual	lucky	timely

   ii What does the word 'persuade' mean?

a	b	c	d
influx	influence	argue	augment

50 'Our sports day was ruined as the excessive rain turned the grass to mud.'

   i What does the word 'ruined' mean?

a	b	c	d
torn	injured	abandoned	exciting

   ii What does the word 'excessive' mean?

a	b	c	d
wet	dismal	gentle	extreme

4

Write the **plural** version of the words in these **sentences.**

4 A

Example   Where are the <u>cats</u>? (cat)

51 At Hamberley Dawlish Farm it is springtime and the cow has had baby
_____. (calf)

52 Jeraphim, the old ram, is very pleased with himself, because his ewe has had
three baby _____ . (sheep)

53 The _____ (donkey) were in the field with the horses as thee
were two new foals to play with.

54 The _____ (goose) were by the pond with the ducks, always
keeping a watchful eye on the baby goslings.

55 The _____ (puppy) were wagging their tails in the hope of a nice
long walk with the farmer's daughter.

5

Read the following passage and then find two examples of each word class to complete the table below.

George and Harry will celebrate their fifth birthday on Saturday at Hixon Hall from noon. Lots of excitement and fun will be promised alongside a pirate's tea party.

56	common noun		
57	proper noun		
58	abstract noun		
59	verb		
60	adjective		

Read the following comprehension text and answer the questions that follow it.

Henry Pottle's Big Moment

The royal palace was all of a flutter. The whole place had been cleaned from top to toe in readiness for the extremely grand party. This once-in-a-lifetime occasion was to mark the very happy engagement between Princess Mathilda and her

5   handsome fiancé-to-be, Prince Viktor. The prince and his family were staying in the royal residence, but many more relatives would be arriving later. Prince Viktor was a most handsome prince and as Princess Mathilda was extremely beautiful, they made a very popular couple. Everybody in the country was talking about the wedding and several hundred journalists, camera operators and film crew were

10   camped just outside the palace gates. Thousands of well-wishers had been lining up in the streets around the palace, desperate to catch a glimpse of the royal couple or their guests. Henry Pottle was only 18 and he was still finding it difficult to believe that he had been fortunate enough to be taken on by the palace as a footman. He really wanted to be a yeoman of the royal cellars so that he could

15   look after the precious collection of wine, but this would take a lot of time. For now, Henry was thrilled that he had a job as a footman and was beyond excited to get the chance to look inside the banqueting hall.

Beautiful burgundy curtains were hung from the huge windows. Opulent gold tablecloths were being ironed on the long tables while crystal glassware was

20   carefully polished and placed in perfect lines. The finest gold cutlery glowed in the sunlight and cut-glass vases were filled with huge white lilies, rich wine roses, soft pink peonies and delicate white gypsophilia. The evocative scent filled the banqueting hall.

Henry sneaked to the door of the kitchens, desperate to see what was going on.
25 He was open-mouthed at the number of people who were working so hard, busily
preparing the most delectable food: tiny canapés of smoked salmon and crab
mousse to accompany the champagne, local lamb with baby vegetables for the
main course and a trio of mini puddings to follow – succulent figs, sticky dates
and plump purple plums nestled together on platters loaded with cheese.

30 As the banqueting hall was now ready, the royal red carpet was unrolled in
readiness for the guests, who would be arriving within the hour. Last-minute
titivations were taking place and as the daylight ebbed away, the mammoth job of
lighting all of the candles began. Henry gazed at the team of people who had the
responsible job of creating this magical lighting effect.

35 The Master of Ceremonies for the evening was highly entertaining. All of the
guests had arrived and Princess Mathilda looked exquisite in her sumptuous
dress that twinkled with thousands of hand-stitched diamonds and pearls that
decorated the hem. Henry knew that he should be nowhere near the banqueting
hall in case anyone should see him, but his curiosity was too great. He could not
40 get anywhere near the entrance, but there was a door at the back of the hall that
Henry wondered about. He would only need to open it a tiny way to gain a viewing
opportunity, just wide enough to see the beautiful dress. Henry decided to break
all protocol for a once-in-a-lifetime occasion. He softly turned the key and with the
gentlest of nudges, Henry pushed the door open.

45 Well, what actually happened was that the nudge of the door touched the leg of a
chair that knocked the table that sent a crystal vase shattering to the floor with an
almighty CRASH! Lady Arbuthnot, a rather hefty lady in a pea-green dress, jumped
at the noise, dropping her knife on the table, which sent her plate hurtling to the
floor. Lord Arbuthnot, who was
50 even more portly than his wife,
bent down to retrieve the plate, but
slipped on some spilt crab mousse
and fell backwards as chaos broke
out. Like escalating dominoes, one
55 person bumped into the next, who
bumped into the next, who bumped
into the next. People skidded, tables
toppled and Prince Viktor looked in
abject horror at the ever-increasing
60 nightmare. Princess Mathilda burst
into tears as she surveyed the
ongoing pandemonium. Henry stared
wide-eyed in absolute horror at the
carnage.

61 Why was the palace so busy?

_____

_____

1 A
1

62 What was Henry's job?

_____

1 A
1

63 Which two **adjectives** describe the table covers?

_____

_____

1 A
1

64 Why do you think the dress 'twinkled' (line 37)?

_____

_____

1 B
2

65 What is meant by the **phrase** 'Henry decided to break all protocol' (line 43)?

_____

_____

1 B
1

66 What is meant by the **phrase** 'like escalating dominoes' (line 54)?

_____

_____

1 B
1

67 Which two words are used in the last paragraph to mean 'fat'?

_____

_____

1 C
2

68 Find two words in the last paragraph that are used to mean 'mayhem'.

_____

_____

2

69 What two-word **phrase** is used to mean 'a beautiful smell'?

_____

1 C
1

70 Find two reasons why Henry decided to open the back door.

_____

_____

1 B
2

71 What is meant by the **phrase** 'last-minute titivations' (line 31–2)?

_____

_____

1 C
1

72 What do these words mean as used in the third paragraph of the text?

   a delectable (line 26) _____

   b trio (line 28) _____

   c succulent (line 28) _____

   d nestled (line 29) _____

1 C
4

73 Match these **phrases** to these literary effects:

   a plump purple plums   **simile**

   b CRASH!   personification

   c delicate, shy gypsophilia   **alliteration**

   d like escalating dominoes   **onomatopoeia**

1 F
4

74 Place these **sentences** in order, starting with what happened first.

Lord Arbuthnot tripped backwards.

The crystal vase shattered.

Lady Arbuthnot dropped some cutlery.

Lord Arbuthnot slipped on some canapés.

Lady Arbuthnot was startled by the noise.

Some porcelain plunged to the floor.

_____

_____

_____

_____

_____

1 A
3

1 28

2 c, d, f, g

3 *1 mark for each of:*
  a focus = emphasis, centre, object
  b tinged = tinted, coloured, shaded
  c revolutionary = innovative, new, radical

4 The snow covers everywhere like a blanket.

5 It shows the natural effects of snow. It is a new way of colouring shadows. Monet uses short brush strokes.

6 'learnt' uses the same spelling rule.

7 c

8 a

9 c

10 e

11 agile – There are trapeze artists in a circus.

12 manager – The football escaped from the defender.

13 police – People convicted of a crime might spend time in a prison.

14 chef – Homemade soup is a cheap and nutritious meal.

15 ess (addresses)   ite (literacy)

16 ial (materials)   pea (appears)

17 cle (bicycle)   tin (yachting)

18 cia (special)   rea (breathe)

19 ain (certainly)   cke (blacken)

20 ght (heighten)   der (considerate)

21 d

22 d

23 a

24 d

25 c

26 head and neck – The other body parts are based on the foot.

27 horse and donkey – The other words are baby animals.

28 bowl and dish – The other words are meals.

29 candy and cream – The other words are tastes.

30 blouse and trousers – The other words are outerwear.

31 hide and conceal – The other words are about revealing or showing.

32 caravans – add the 's'

33 shops – add the 's'

34 walks – add the 's'

35 benches – add 'es'

36 swings – add the 's'

37 chimney – add the 's'

38 parties – take off the 'y' then add 'ies'

39 children – the plural of 'child' is 'children'

40 monkeys – add the 's'

41 babies – take off the 'y' then add 'ies'

42 lesson, threw

43 sow, rows

44 yolk, sight

45 hour, sales

46 savage, brutal

47 absent, missing, away

48 behaviour, performance, conduct

49 manage, cope, survive

50 silent, mute

51 awkward

52 mislay

53 sacred

54 torrent

55 otherwise

56 revulsion

57 destiny

58 but

59 which

60 provided

61 or

62 and

63 can (vacancies)

64 age (voyage)

65 pan (panicked)

66 cry (crystallised)

67 ply (simply)

68 hobbies

69 cycling

70 occasional

71 library

72 interest

73 heroes

74 caught

75 bravery

1 flexible

2 female

3 retreat

4 minor

5 finish

6 death

7 a

8 d

9 d

10 b

11 represent

12 respond

13 justify

14 frighten

15 swap

16 power

17 exclude

18 park and fields – The other words are waterways.

19 nest and den – The other words are homes for people to live in.

20 pear and apple – The other words are citrus fruit.

21 pillow and duvet – The other words are to do with shielding.

22 winter and weather – The other words are types of weather.

23 workers – add the 's'

24 buses – add 'es'

25 factories – take off the 'y' and add 'ies'

26 matches – add 'es'

27 boxes – add 'es'

28 lorries – take off the 'y' and add 'ies'

29 ear (clearance)

30 bin (cabins)

31 orb (forbidden)

32 ail (trailing)

33 ant (antibiotic)

34 rig (original)

35 get (vegetables)

36 lunch – All infant schoolchildren are paired up with a buddy.

37 pupils – Our library has a quiet reading area with beanbags to sit on.

38 a – Michael was tired so he had a lie down.

39 fun – Jawahir and her friends loved to go sledging when it snowed.

40 dear – The boys chose to play beach volleyball in their free time.

41 i **b** latest
  ii **a** concerning

42 i **c** treasured
  ii **d** case

43 as

44 although

45 after

46 when

47 but

48 cereal, flour

49 dye, hair

50 heel, sole

51 buy, currant

52 whether, weather

53 they're, it's

54 waves, rough

55 *any two of:* hawk, treetop, ground, eyes, movement, grass, mouse, snack

56 *any two of:* sat, surveying, spotted, feed, make, wouldn't, would

57 *both of:* his, it

58 *any two of:* top, piercing, tall, grey, hungry, tasty

59 *both of:* powerfully, thoroughly

60 *any two of:* on, below, in

61 *both of:* until, but

62 poorly

63 animal

64 infection

65 prescription

66 health

67 happier

68 Bone Shaker, Shark Survivor, Drop of Death

69 Shropshire

70 *1/2 mark for any eight of the following:* 'thrills', 'dare to ride', 'only the bravest survive', 'white knuckle ride', 'vertigo adventure', 'swing and dangle', 'shark infested waters', 'only the fish will hear you scream', 'steeper, deeper, taller, faster, crazier', 'awesome ride', 'plunge', 'thrown backwards', 'many more rides', 'endless excitement', 'thrills and spills'

71 *1 mark for each of:*
   a wobbly, unstable, unsteady, rocky, unbalanced
   b amazing, brilliant, breath-taking, tremendous, splendid
   c dive, drop, plummet, fall

72 *1 mark each for 'YES' and any three of:* the baby Twills fun fair, the petting farm for little Twillers, nature trails, boat trips on the lake, suitable for all of the family.

73 *1 mark each for 'YES' and any three of:* disabled access, plenty of seating areas, restaurants and cafes, boat trips on the lake, lots of countryside to enjoy, suitable for all of the family.

74 *1 mark each for any two of:* a massive 25 per cent off ticket prices with the flyer, you can save up to 20 per cent if you print the tickets out, VIP tickets mean no queues.

75 *1 mark each for any two of:* deeper, taller, faster (not crazier as it has a different spelling rule)

Paper 3

1 raiding
2 fiercely
3 compact
4 produced
5 shallow
6 surprise
7 retreat
8 expand, stretch
9 prevent, prohibit
10 advantage
11 silence
12 almost
13 damage
14 serpent
15 many
16 regional
17 thought
18 strangle
19 indebted
20 at – I checked that my hair was tidy in the mirror.
21 plug – My dad needed to recharge his laptop computer.
22 tiger – Arabella wanted a bigger cage for her tiny pet hamsters.
23 out – In assembly today we learnt about protecting the environment.
24 whenever
25 but
26 unless
27 although
28 when
29 if
30 sin (supposing)   her (therefore)
31 oug (thought)   ous (variously)
32 eig (weighty)   mbe (remember)
33 ate (separate)   upb (cupboard)
34 gth (strength)   wer (answering)
35 and (islands)   ngt (length)
36 boring
37 slavery
38 cause
39 hostile
40 ignore
41 A = sharks   B = angel fish
   C = tetras   D = weather loach
42 E = fighting fish   F = goldfish
   G = minnows   H = guppies
43 waste, right
44 piece, supper
45 profit, which
46 suite, stationery
47 i a adequate   ii c pestered
48 i b empty   ii c instantly
49 i a occasion   ii b influence
50 i c abandoned   ii d extreme
51 calves – change the 'f' to a 'v' before adding 'es'
52 sheep – the spelling does not change in the plural
53 donkeys – just add the 's'
54 geese – the plural of goose is 'geese'
55 puppies – change the 'y' to 'ies'
56 common nouns: birthday, noon, tea-party
57 proper nouns: George, Harry, Saturday, Hixon Hall
58 abstract nouns: excitement, fun
59 verb: celebrate, promised, will, be
60 adjective: fifth, pirate's
61 There was a grand party for the engagement of Princess Mathilda.
62 Henry was a footman.
63 opulent and gold
64 The candlelight reflected in the thousands of diamonds and pearls.
65 Henry broke all of the rules.
66 One domino falls and hits the next domino, making it fall, and people were falling in the same way.
67 Hefty and portly mean the same as fat.
68 pandemonium, carnage or chaos
69 'evocative scent'
70 *any two of:* Henry opened the back door because he was curious to see the dress; Henry could not get anywhere near the entrance; Henry could not risk being seen.
71 'Last minute titivations' mean to finish off the last few jobs to make everywhere look perfect.
72 *1 mark for each of:*
   a delicious, tasty, appetizing
   b a group of three
   c luscious, juicy, moist
   d snuggled, huddled, nuzzled, squashed
73 a alliteration
   b onomatopoeia
   c personification
   d simile
74 1 The crystal vase shattered.
   2 Lady Arbuthnot was startled by the noise.
   3 Lady Arbuthnot dropped some cutlery.
   4 Some porcelain plunged to the floor.
   5 Lord Arbuthnot slipped on some canapés.
   6 Lord Arbuthnot tripped backwards.
75 Henry was present for such a big, impressive event; It was Henry that caused such a big event.

Paper 4

1 c
2 c
3 e
4 a, d, f
5 b, c, d
6 d
7 a passion
   b beautiful
   c built
   d mending
8 d
9 c
10 b, c, d, e
11 beautiful
12 season
13 summer
14 autumn
15 leaves
16 oranges
17 roads
18 perhaps, maybe

19 final, terminal
20 perfect, ideal
21 comfort, soothe, reassure
22 tiger, giraffe
23 poppy, rose
24 crisps, nuts
25 dawn, morning
26 enemy, foe
27 table, dresser
28 slow, lethargic
29 got (maggots)
30 hen (toughened)
31 tip (multiple)
32 pet (carpets)
33 odd (plodded)
34 hut (parachute)
35 massive
36 thousand
37 lasted
38 seconds
39 caused
40 destruction
41 promised
42 rebuilt
43 b
44 a
45 e
46 c
47 c
48 empty
49 specific
50 terrify
51 sagging
52 forgive
53 coarse
54 entire
55 believe
56 act
57 cover
58 forget
59 attack
60 form
61 possible
62 succeed
63 perfect
64 domesticated
65 tactful
66 strong
67 bold
68 sensible
69 Big Ben, Tiny Tim
70 *any two of:* boys, football, rugby, school
71 *any two of:* loved, run, preferred, jump, enjoyed, hated, played, wasn't
72 fast, passionately
73 big, tiny
74 they, it, their
75 *any two of:* while, although, and

1 oven
2 eggs
3 milk
4 sunflower
5 carefully
6 golden
7 plenty
8 cheap
9 beneath
10 often, frequent
11 eager, keen, avid
12 iron
13 top
14 earth
15 litter
16 kind
17 serious
18 colossal
19 share
20 error
21 fret
22 aggravate
23 lunch – On Sunday Grandma makes a delicious apple crumble.
24 octagon – A hexagon has six edges but a pentagon has only five edges.
25 brush – Mixing yellow and blue paint together makes green paint.
26 animal – Our class collected autumn leaves for the nature table.
27 from – The green cross code protects us when we cross the road.
28 newspaper and magazine – The others are genres of literature.
29 whisper and murmur – The others are all loud.
30 run and walk – The others are all jumping.
31 Paris and Rome – The others are all countries.
32 shops – just add the 's'
33 churches – add 'es'
34 fields – just add the 's'
35 halves – change the 'f' to a 'v' and add 'es'
36 these – 'this' becomes 'these' in the plural
37 gra (grammar)   tor (history)
38 agi (imagine)   tio (mentioning)
39 ess (possession)   ont (continue)
40 sio (decision)   rwa (forwarding)
41 rpo (purpose)   tin (quoting)
42 ppe (disappear)   art (earthly)
43 tre (extreme)   amo (famously)
44 sti (question)   nin (reigning)
45 whose, to
46 draught, where
47 two, their
48 been, beach

49 bear, fur
50 common
51 miss
52 defend
53 correct
54 sweet
55 forget
56 lie
57 b
58 d
59 b
60 c
61 a
62 b
63 *1 mark for each of:* she is overweight, she is a furry cat, she is a ginger/red cat, she has a little nose.
64 She had been catching up and having fun with her friends.
65 She moved in a relaxed, slow, ambling way.
66 She felt as heavy as a sack of potatoes.
67 George was Harry's friend.
68 Harry was not a gentle child but liked rolling around and being active.
69 The tall man crossed the road rather than have to pass her.
70 She could lose a little weight; she could take more exercise.
71 There was now a queue of bins; Teagan had put on some weight.
72 Nicholas goes to cubs, Louise takes ballet lessons, Rachel plays the piano and Alexander kicks the football.
73 a privacy, isolation, seclusion, being alone
   b dying away, decreasing, reducing
   c to take a nap, sleep, rest
74 Teagan didn't want to disturb anyone; she wanted to use the cat flap.
75 a Where a single vowel is followed by a single consonant that ends the word, double the last consonant before adding the suffix.
   b Bobbed, spotted, flopped and planned also follow this spelling rule.

1 d
2 d
3 a
4 b
5 d
6 e

ANSWERS

7 a pushed
  b automatic
  c frown
  d peak
  e smooth
8 a shuffle
  b nauseous
  c panicky
  d faint
  e excess
9 e
10 a
11 *any five of:* 'absolute fear', 'this
   doesn't feel like a treat', 'my hands
   feel wet and sticky', 'my forehead
   feels clammy', 'I feel slightly faint
   and panicky', 'this is only nerves',
   'I feel really faint now', 'I want to be
   sick', 'save me'.
12 *any four of:* she states that
   something magical happened and
   this transforms her, she is so scared
   at first and then she feels relief and
   a sense of achievement, she begins
   not knowing what will happen and
   at the end she does know what the
   next performance will be like, at the
   beginning she doesn't want to go on
   stage but at the end she says that
   next year she might be too keen to
   get on the stage.
13 pants
14 cry
15 step
16 ram
17 break

18 brutal
19 sincere
20 egotistic
21 evil
22 fairly
23 rarely
24 forage
25 rib (scribbled)
26 the (cathedral)
27 cat (education)
28 lid (holiday)
29 rid (bridge)
30 emerge
31 abolish
32 accept
33 unattractive
34 unentitled
35 cowardice
36 swimming
37 cycling
38 perseverance
39 equally
40 energy
41 winning
42 inspiring
43 i a positive   ii b violence
44 i d core   ii c considerable
45 i a stunned   ii b intellectual
46 multiply – Meixiu had a huge bag of
   sweets to share between her friends.
47 jam – Amber's birthday cake was in
   the shape of a cat.
48 bake –Stir-frying is a healthier way to
   cook.
49 feet – We should always wash our
   hands before preparing food.

50 but
51 because
52 whenever
53 as
54 if
55 so
56 and
57 stream, pier – The others can be
   found in the sky.
58 submarine, galleon – The others are
   pleasure boats.
59 October, February – The others are
   summer months.
60 numbers, counting – The others are
   types of number.
61 violin, cello – The others are brass
   instruments.
62 teeth – the plural of tooth is teeth
63 shelves – change the 'f' to 'v' then
   add 'es'
64 children – the plural of child is
   children
65 sweets – just add the 's'
66 fillings – just add the 's'
67 around
68 but
69 marathon
70 local
71 worked
72 12
73 Louisa
74 11
75 e A cookery app can help when
   baking cakes.

Bond CEM English and Verbal Reasoning 9–10

A4

75 Find two reasons why this title has been chosen for this text.

_____

_____

_____ 2

Read the following comprehension text and answer the questions that follow it.

The Miracle of Camp 60

The Orkney Islands are a group of islands in the far north of Scotland. From Kirkwall, head towards Scapa Flow, which lies between the mainland, Orkney and the island of Burray. The causeways, referred to as the 'Churchill Barriers', link
5 the mainland to the islands. Lamb Holm is a small island of less than 0.4 km² and is uninhabited. Some Italian prisoners of war were camped on the little island of Lamb Holm during the Second World War. Father Giacobazzi, the camp's priest, and Domenico Chiocchetti, an artist and one of the prisoners, persuaded the camp commander to allow them to build their own church on the island.

10 The prisoners were given two Nissen air raid shelters, so some of the men joined the huts end-to-end to create their own little church. Outside the men fashioned a bell tower and then they layered thick cement over the outside of the Nissen huts to protect the church from the harsh weather conditions. Domenico took to the project with great enthusiasm. He gathered together other eager workers:
15 Buttapasta – a cement worker, Palumbi – a blacksmith, Promavera and Micheloni – electricians, Barcaglioni, Battiato, Devitto, Fornasier, Pennisi, Sforza and other unnamed helpers, and the transformation of the little church began.

At one end of the hut they built a perfectly-formed sanctuary and altar while the whole chapel was lined and decorated in the most exquisite manner. Walls
20 were painted to look as though they were made of brick, with stone carvings and vaulted ceilings. They created perfect-looking stained glass windows and angels that would have made even the most unreligious visitor gasp with disbelief.

Flotsam and jetsam wood from old wrecked ships formed a tabernacle, while the blacksmith collected scrap metal and old tin cans and fashioned them into
25 candelabras and ornate gates that enclosed the sanctuary. By using the most basic of materials, this group of talented and enthusiastic men pooled their skills to create a place of beauty.

The men used this church during their time on the island. At the end of the war, the Italian men were returned back home, but the little Italian church has remained.
30 Back in 1960, Domenico Chiocchetti returned from Italy to the Orkney Islands to help with the restoration of the church and with him he brought a carving of Christ, as a gift from the town of Moena, his home town. The people of the Orkneys made a wooden cross and canopy on which the carving is placed and the little shrine was erected outside the little chapel in 1961. Once Chiocchetti finished, he wrote
35 a letter to the people of the Orkney Islands formally giving the little Italian church

to them so that they could love it, look after it, and remember the Italian prisoners of war who had loved their church. After all of these years, the little chapel stands as a symbol of hope, peace, love and faith that not even the war could destroy.

40 Domenico Chiocchetti died in Moena in 1999. He was 89 years old and was buried in Italy, but a service was also held in the Italian church in Lamb Holm to remember the extraordinary man who had done something so remarkable in his life.

Answer the following questions. Underline the correct letter.

1 How many people now live on the island of Lamb Holm?

  a a small number

  b some, but not too many

  c none at all

  d lots

  e an unknown number

2 Who was Father Giacobazzi?

  a He was an artist.

  b He was an Italian prisoner of war.

  c He was a religious man serving the needs of the camp.

  d He was the camp commander.

  e He made the carving of Christ.

3 Which prisoner do you think helped with layering the cement on the outside of the church?

  a Father Giacobazzi

  b Domenico Chiocchetti

  c Palumbi

  d Promavera

  e Buttapasta

4 Which three of these statements are true?

   a The Churchill Barriers join the islands to the mainland.

   b Scapa Flow is on the island of Burray.

   c The little church was made out of three Nissen air raid shelters.

   d The tabernacle was made from scrap wood.

   e In 1999, Domenico Chiocchetti returned to Lamb Holm.

   f Palumbi created decorative items from empty tin cans.

5 Which three of these statements are false?

   a At least 12 people helped transform the little church.

   b The Nissen huts were placed side by side to create the church.

   c At one end of the church was the sanctuary and the other end had the altar.

   d Plain gates were placed around the sanctuary.

   e The ceiling of the church was decorated.

6 Why did the men cover the outside of the little church?

   a so that it wasn't hit during the war

   b so that it was unseen from the mainland

   c so that it could be painted

   d so that the church was protected

   e so that the church was kept warm

7 What do these words mean as used in the text?

   a enthusiasm   passion / knowledge / canniness / perseverance

   b exquisite   careful / careless / solid / beautiful

   c erected   built / welcoming / polished / symbolic

   d restoration   cleaning / mending / destroying / creating

8 Which town did Domenico Chiocchetti come from?

   a Orkney

   b Lamb Holm

   c Burray

   d Moena

   e Italy

9 What did the people of the Orkney Islands make?

1 A

    a a carving and a cross

    b a canopy and a carving

    c a canopy and a cross

    d a shrine and a cross

    e a shrine and a canopy

1

10 What four things did the little Italian church represent?

1 B

a war	**b** hope
c faith	**d** love
e peace	**f** enthusiasm
g friendship	**h** Camp 60

4

Some of the words in this paragraph have letters missing. Write out the complete words in the right-hand box, so that the spellings are correct and the paragraph makes sense. The first word has been done for you.

15 mins

3 C

Monet's g __ __ dens in Giverny are b __ __ __ tiful during every se __ s __ n. In spring the tulips are heart-warming. In the s __ __ __ __ r the water-lilies are evocative of Monet's art work and in the a __ __ __ __ n the tree l __ __ __ __ s turn from green to bright reds, __ __ a __ g __ s, yellows and plum. Giverny is easy to reach from Paris or Dieppe and French r __ __ __ s are easy to drive on.	Eg. gardens **11** **12** **13** **14** **15** **16** **17**

7

Look at the following words and then use them to answer the questions that follow.

already	Saturday	coward	terminal	litter
altogether	ideal	comfort	harvest	perhaps
pitch	garment	permit	stitch	alarm
perfect	kitchen	farther	sermon	final
maybe	reassure	aerial	although	soothe

18 Find two words that are **synonyms** for the word 'possibly'.

_____

19 Find two words that are **antonyms** for the word 'initial'.

_____

20 Find two words that are **antonyms** for the word 'flawed'.

_____

21 Find three words that are **synonyms** for the word 'support'.

_____

_____

Underline the two odd words out in the following groups of words.

Example purple lilac <u>olive</u> <u>sage</u> violet

22 sheep goat cow tiger giraffe

23 petal leaf poppy rose stamen

24 fudge toffee chocolate crisps nuts

25 dusk dawn twilight morning evening

26 mate friend enemy foe pal

27 table chair bench dresser sofa

28 fast slow speedy hasty lethargic

40

Find the three-letter word that can be added to the capital letters to make a new word. The new word will complete the **sentence** sensibly.

Example   We HED the keys to the estate agent. <u>AND</u>

29 She used MAGS as bait on her fishing line. _____

30 The patio doors needed TOUGED glass for safety. _____

31 Twelve is a MULLE of two, three, four, six and twelve. _____

32 The shop sold CARS, laminate and tiles for every room. _____

33 The donkey slowly PLED around the field. _____

34 I love flying, but if I had a PARACE I would be nervous in case it didn't open!

_____

35–42 The words in the box are missing from the paragraph. Using all of the words, and using them only once, can you complete the paragraph so that it makes sense?

caused	destruction	lasted	massive
promised	rebuilt	seconds	thousand

On Monday February 29th 1960, in Agadir, Morocco, there was a

_____ earthquake. Over 12 _____ people were killed

and yet the earthquake _____ for only _____ . A huge

tidal wave was _____ by the earthquake and that triggered much

_____ . King Mohammed of Morocco _____ that the

town would be _____ .

6

10 mins

3 A

3 F

8

41

Complete each **sentence** by selecting the best word from the options **a, b, c, d** or **e**.

Example   People travelling to certain countries need _____ **d – vaccination** _____ .

a	b	c	d	e
immunity	certainty	vacation	vaccination	respiration

43 It was a real _____ for his mum to afford to pay for his violin lessons.

a	b	c	d	e
pleasure	sacrifice	easy	problematic	inspiration

44 The main _____ of this session is to introduce you to each other.

a	b	c	d	e
purpose	beginning	ending	reason	impulse

45 Is it _____ to talk about football in a maths lesson?

a	b	c	d	e
helpful	useless	relative	vital	relevant

46 I'll choose the _____ notebook for homework notes and the ornate one as a journal.

a	b	c	d	e
plane	familiar	ordinary	decorative	extreme

47 Please do not _____ the party as it is a secret.

a	b	c	d	e
chat	gossip	mention	refer	discussion

5

Underline the one word on the right that has the most similar meaning to the word on the left.

2C

Example   vision   plotting / smell / <u>sight</u> / style / map

48 vacant   holiday / empty / vacuum / fake / genuine

49 precise   undefined / smooth / specific / general / shadowing

50 frighten   unfriendly / reveal / soothe / terrible / terrify

51 slack   sagging / lost / uncaring / ignore / lazy

52 pardon   rude / forgive / pun / polite / manners

53 rough   study / coarse / nasty / unkind / fine

54 whole   partial / entire / gap / opening / globe   **7**

Write out the **root** of the following words.

(8 mins)

[4][B]

Example   specifically = specific

55 unbelievable   _____

56 inactive   _____

57 discovering   _____

58 unforgettable   _____

59 counterattack   _____

60 reformed   _____

61 impossibly   _____   **7**

Add the missing letters to the word on the right to make a word with the opposite meaning to the word on the left.

[2D][3C]

Example   ascended   d _e_ _s_ c _e_ nd _e_ _d_

62 fail   s __ c __ e __ d

63 flawed   p e r __ __ __ __

64 feral   d o m __ s __ i __ a __ e d

65 frank   t a __ t __ u l

66 frail   __ t __ o n g

67 faint   __ o l __

68 foolish   s __ __ s __ b l e   **7**

Read the following passage and then find two examples of each word class to complete the table below.

Big Ben loved to run fast while Tiny Tim preferred to jump although both boys enjoyed football. They passionately hated rugby and fortunately it wasn't played at their school.

69	proper noun		
70	common noun		
71	verb		
72	adverb		
73	adjective		
74	pronoun		
75	conjunction		

7

Now go to the Progress Chart to record your score!   Total   90

Paper 5

Some of the words in this paragraph have letters missing. Write out the complete words in the right-hand box, so that the spellings are correct and the paragraph makes sense. The first word has been done for you.

	Eg. Yorkshire
To make the best Yo __ ks __ __ __ e Puddings,	
preheat the o __ __ n to 200°. Beat two e __ __ __	1
into a bowl with half a pint of __ i __ __ and	2
whisk. Add 100 g of plain flour and mix into a smooth	3
batter. Place a meagre amount of	
s __ n __ l __ w __ r oil into a dish and heat it in	4
the oven. When it is spitting, take it out, pour in the	5
batter ca __ __ __ __ __ __ y and then cook for 30	6
minutes or until it is g __ l __ en and risen. Serve with	
roast potatoes, vegetables and pl __ n __ y of gravy.	7

Look at the following words and then use them to answer the questions that follow.

cargo	artist	enjoy	tease	oven
linen	weave	woven	often	preach
golden	hasten	beneath	dozen	listen
cheap	seam	eagle	eager	hotel
frequent	stitch	keen	strength	avid

8 Find one word that is an **antonym** for the word 'expensive'.

_____

9 Find one word that is a **synonym** for the word 'under'.

_____

10 Find two words that are **antonyms** for the word 'seldom'.

_____

3 C

7

2 B

2 A

2 B

11 Find three words that are **synonyms** for the word 'enthusiastic'.

_____

_____

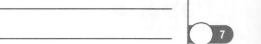

Which one word on the right will fit equally well with both pairs of words on the left? Underline the answer.

Example   rhythm, pulse   whip, whisk   dance / cook / <u>beat</u> / belt

12 press, smooth   steel, tin   iron / brass / squeeze / flatten

13 blouse, tunic   best, highest   shirt / top / coat / ace

14 soil, dirt   Neptune, Mars   moon / earth / peat / Mercury

15 rubbish, trash   brood, gaggle   litter / waste / tip / upset

16 sweet, caring   type, sort   nice / cute / breed / kind

Underline the one word on the right that has the most similar meaning to the word on the left.

Example   vision   plotting / smell / <u>sight</u> / style / map

17 earnest   serious / frivolous / petty / pretty / attempting

18 giant   long / broad / low / colossal / coveted

19 divide   subtract / multiply / deduct / revise / share

20 mistake   error / naughty / disrupt / interpretation / understanding

21 worry   fret / peace / worsen / anger / frustration

22 worsen   difficult / unexpected / aggravate / utilise / horrible

Rearrange these words to make the longest **sentence** you can. Underline the word that is **superfluous**.

Example   So cream <u>eat</u> the were cakes delicious.
                 The cream cakes were so delicious.

46

23 Sunday on apple makes grandma delicious crumble a lunch.

_____

24 Edges but a five edges only six has octagon has pentagon hexagon a.

_____

25 Mixing yellow makes green brush together and blue paint paint.

_____

26 Our table collected nature leaves for the animal autumn class.

_____

27 The road protects us from the green cross code when we cross.

_____

5

Underline the two odd words out in the following groups of words.

2 F

Example   purple   lilac   <u>olive</u>   <u>sage</u>   violet

28 newspaper   poems   stories   magazine   plays

29 shout   bellow   whisper   murmur   roar

30 leap   run   spring   walk   jump

31 France   Paris   Italy   Rome   Spain

4

Write the **plural** version of the words in these **sentences**.

4 A

Example   Where are the <u>cats</u>? (cat)

32 The bookshop had a free guide to the village that provided a scenic walk

beginning with a tour of the _____. (shop)

33 At the end of the shops the guided walk leads walkers past the chemist and the

two _____. (church)

34 The guide then recommends crossing over the brook by the bridge that runs

between the _____. (cornfield)

35 This divides the village into two _____ (half) and allows for wonderful
views to both the right and left.

36 From here it is a loop back to the bookshop where _____ (this)
directions, or any other walks, can be printed off.

5

Find the three letters that complete these words. The three letters do not have to
make a word.

⏱ 10 mins

3 B

Example   fr<u>esh</u>   spl<u>as</u>h

37 _____ mmar   his_____ y

38 im_____ ne   men_____ ning

39 poss_____ ion   c_____ inue

40 deci_____ n   fo_____ rding

41 pu_____ se   quo_____ g

42 disa_____ ar   e_____ hly

43 ex_____ me   f_____ usly

44 que_____ on   reig_____ g

8

Underline the correct words in each of these **sentences**.

3 D

Example   She (<u>blew</u>, blue) her trumpet solo in the school (<u>band</u>, banned).

45 "(Whose, who's) book does that belong (to, too, two)?" the teacher enquired in
norming assembly.

46 There was an uncomfortable (draft, draught) from under the door (wear, where) the cold wind howled.

47 The (to, too, two) classes of children obediently hung (their, there, they're) coats in the infant school cloakroom.

48 "Have you (bean, been) to the (beach, beech) this morning?" asked Mum, as she surveyed the sandy footsteps that trailed through the house.

49 My teddy (bare, bear) has a brown (fir, fur) body, a little bell in his ear and a smartly striped jumper that looks very jaunty.

5

Add the missing letters to the word on the right to make a word with the opposite meaning to the word on the left.

2D **3C**

Example   ascended   d _e_ _s_ c _e_ nd _e_ _d_

50 rare   c __ __ __ __ n

51 attend   m __ __ s

52 attack   de __ __ __ __

53 wrong   __ __ __ __ __ ct

54 sour   s __ __ __ t

55 remember   f __ __ __ __ __

56 truth   __ __ e

7

Complete each **sentence** by selecting the best word from the options **a**, **b**, **c**, **d** or **e**.

3 **E**

Example   People travelling to certain countries need ____ **d – vaccination** ____ .

a	b	c	d	e
immunity	certainty	vacation	vaccination	respiration

49

57 We would like to _____ your piano lesson by an extra quarter of an hour.

a	**b**	**c**	**d**	**e**
complete	extend	lift	conceal	reveal

58 My sister will _____ go into my bedroom and mess with my homework.

a	**b**	**c**	**d**	**e**
several	almost	likely	frequently	somewhere

59 I like ice-cream, _____ toffee flavour.

a	**b**	**c**	**d**	**e**
accept	especially	regarding	supposing	adoring

60 Do not _____ ; you only have twenty mental maths equations not hundreds.

a	**b**	**c**	**d**	**e**
wine	whinny	exaggerate	excerpt	fussy

61 In this magic trick, I shall make this huge elephant _____ into thin air.

a	**b**	**c**	**d**	**e**
disappear	distrust	disgust	discover	display

62 I was so _____ to get home in time, I caught a taxi.

a	**b**	**c**	**d**	**e**
separate	desperate	need	late	likely

6

Read the comprehension text below and answer the questions that follow it.

A Fishy Tale…

Teagan had spent the afternoon with friends, catching up and having fun. She had been introduced to Milly and Molly, two sisters who had just moved into the area. They seemed friendly enough and Teagan felt sure that they would fit in with the group. She had enjoyed herself but now they had split up and she sauntered
5   along the pavement, in no particular rush to get home. There was nobody about and Teagan was quite enjoying the solitude. She loved dusk when the sun was dwindling away, but it wasn't yet dark, and the remaining sun made her red hair glow. A smell radiated from one of the houses that she passed. Teagan wrinkled

10 her little nose and licked her lips. It smelt of fish, but to her it was a pleasant smell. Teagan thought about what she would have for her supper. She quite fancied fish herself now. A nice piece of poached cod, a thick meaty piece of tuna or perhaps salmon – she could fancy them all. Although meat was good, fish was even better, and she would have been quite happy to eat fish every day but the

15 rest of the family had to be considered. Teagan walked a little faster now that her mouth was salivating at the thought of food. Teagan was always promising herself that she would lose a little weight. She didn't care how she looked, but her health was important and sometimes she found it hard to run around with the children and whenever she jumped, she felt as heavy as a sack of potatoes! She wouldn't

20 have to diet too much and if she did a bit of extra exercise she would soon have more energy, but she did love her food and she would often fall asleep in front of the television at night. In fact, over the past year or two, she could doze off in the middle of the day if she was given half a chance. She didn't think of herself as greedy or lazy but, if truth be told, she was both!

25 She turned from Harrogate Avenue into Sandringham Close and as she turned the bend she could see her house. The tall man from number 17 was walking towards her and Teagan's heart sank. She didn't like the tall man and, to be frank, he couldn't stand her. Teagan stared straight ahead, willing herself not to look at the man. She hoped that he wouldn't acknowledge her, but he decided to cross

30 the road so that he didn't even have to share the pavement with her. Teagan felt hurt at his obvious dislike, but now he had gone and she had her supper to look forward to.

After that, the lady from number 25 came tottering up the street. She sold make-up and perfume door-to-door and she was always pleased to see Teagan.

35 'Hello Teagan, how are you? The weather is getting chillier so make sure you get back. I'm only going to do another couple of houses then I'll be popping back home myself.' Teagan listened patiently as the lady continued talking, but it was quite cool standing still and Teagan's legs were aching. She was desperate for a sit down and the children would have all returned home from school by now.

40 Eventually, the lady made her goodbyes and Teagan continued along the road.

Harry, the little boy who lived at number 3, spotted Teagan and came toddling towards her, a huge smile on his face. Teagan quite liked Harry – he could be a little rough-and-tumble, but he was good-natured. Teagan let Harry embrace her. He smelt of lemon soap and toothpaste. 'Teagan, I've been to George's house to

45 play,' he proudly told her. Teagan listened intently as he told her the details of how George was going to have a baby brother or sister soon and that George had been on holiday in a caravan. Teagan was really hungry now and, after a short while, so as not to appear too rude, she walked Harry back to his house and then she darted down her own driveway.

50 There was a light on in the front room and the upstairs bathroom light was also on, so it looked as though the children had already got back. Nicholas had been

to cubs and Louise had had her ballet lesson. Teagan could hear Rachel playing the piano – she had an exam coming up and she wanted to do well. Teagan was proud of the four children. They were gentle, kind, intelligent and friendly and she

55 was so fond of them. She enjoyed their company and although she had a lovely bunch of friends, they were no substitute for family. Teagan didn't want to disturb anyone, so she slipped down the side of the house. A rubbish bin, a recycling bin, a garden waste bin, a clothing bin – Teagan used to have far more room down the side of the house, but now there was a queue of bins to negotiate. 'You

60 couldn't swing a cat around here,' she thought with ironic amusement. She had put on weight since she last came down here so it was case of breathing in and squeezing tight. She could see a discarded football – Alexander, the eldest boy, had a habit of kicking the ball somewhere awkward to reach. She weaved and bobbed in and out, but could have broken her neck trying to reach the back door!

65 Eventually, she got through and into the back garden. She was pleased that Dennis had started the tea as she was now starving. He had the potatoes on the go and she could see him in the kitchen window washing the vegetables. He had spotted her and his face broke into a huge grin. 'Teagan!' he called. 'Where've you been? I was getting worried.' The sun had now disappeared and there was

70 a slight chill in the air. Teagan was glad to be home as she squeezed her fat, furry body through the cat flap and flopped into her basket. Today had been such a hectic day and the rest of the evening was nicely planned out. A lovely supper followed by a catnap in front of the fire and some fuss and attention from everyone – what bliss! Now, was she going to get fish for tea?

63 Describe Teagan's appearance, finding four pieces of evidence from the text to support your view.

17 mins

1 A

_____

_____

_____

_____

4

64 How had Teagan spent the afternoon?

1 A

_____

_____

_____

1

65 What does the **phrase**, 'she sauntered along the pavement' (line 5–6) mean?

1 C

_____

_____

_____

1

66 Can you find a **simile** in the first paragraph?

1 F

_____

_____

_____

1

67 Who was George?

1 A

_____

_____

_____

1

68 What is meant by the **phrase** 'he could be a little rough-and-tumble' (line 42–3)?

1 C

_____

_____

_____

1

69 Why was Teagan hurt in paragraph 2?

_____

_____

_____

70 What two things could Teagan do to gain more energy?

_____

_____

_____

71 Find two reasons why the side of the house is a tight squeeze for Teagan.

_____

_____

_____

72 Can you name the four children and the activity that they each do?

_____

_____

_____

_____

73 What do these words mean as used in the first paragraph of the text?

a solitude (line 7)

_____

b dwindling (line 8)

_____

c doze (line 22)

_____

74 Find two reasons why Teagan decided to use the back door.

_____

_____

_____

75 a In the fifth paragraph, the word 'slip' has become 'slipped'. What spelling rule has been applied here?

1 E

1

_____

b Can you find another word in the fifth paragraph that follows the same spelling rule?

1 E

1

_____

Now go to the Progress Chart to record your score!   Total   90

Read the following comprehension text and answer the questions that follow it.

Fear of the Unknown

I do not know why I have chosen to be here. It feels as though my mind is at home, sitting and watching television, feeling relaxed and having fun, and yet my body is standing here in absolute fear. I look in the mirror again. My hair is swept
5 back into the tightest of buns, hair-sprayed into submission so that no stray hair dares to move out of its place. My face has been scrubbed clean before applying the heavy make-up. My skin looks deathly white and powdered so that there is no shininess. My eyes look dark and I am wearing lipstick. I should be thrilled that I am allowed to wear make-up, but somehow, this doesn't feel like a treat. Gazing
10 at my reflection, I see the white leotard, the layers of net forming the tutu and the white satin ballet shoes that are tied around my white, opaque tights. I look like a ghost.

Now I have to wait. How easy it should be to simply wait but this feels like a never-ending torment. I stare at my white shoes as I stretch my feet, trying to distract
15 myself from the way I feel. This dressing room is not small, but there are lots of girls in here. Mum and Dad are sitting in the audience but I am missing them so much. I wish they were here with me. They are only on the other side of the stage, but that feels like a world away. The speaker crackles before the man's voice asks for the black swans to get ready and as a sudden rush of girls shuffle into line and
20 head off towards the stage, I know that I will be called next. My hands feel wet and sticky, my forehead feels clammy and I feel slightly faint and panicky. I do not want to go on stage. I do not want to dance. I do not want the audience staring at me as I perform. I feel sick again and I cannot struggle out of my costume to go to the loo yet again, as I know this is only nerves.

25 I try to sit down but it is difficult when you are wearing a tutu. I try resting against the wall and the coolness of the painted plaster feels comforting. I want to rest my forehead on the mirror, but I know that I will ruin my make-up and that won't do. The speaker crackles again and now the man's voice is asking for me. 'Calling for white swans, calling for white swans, will all white swans make their way to the
30 stage, will all white swans make their way to the stage now?' I shake my arms, bend my knees to loosen up and join the queue of other white swans. I shuffle along the line until I am just offstage. I feel really faint now and I want to be sick. I look around in desperation, waiting to catch the eye of someone, anyone, who can get me out and save me.

35 It is too late. The music starts and I am shoved in the back by a big girl too keen to get on the stage. My arms jerk up in mechanical reaction to the music as I glide

onto the stage, a grimace on my face that is trying so hard to become a fixed
smile. My legs kick out, my arms move gracefully and my body forms different
positions as the music flows … and then something magical happens. I jump, I
40 glide, I bend, I straighten, I sweep, I bow, I stretch, I leap and I forget that I am on
the stage. Eventually the music reaches its climax and then dies away. So too my
body is pushed to its limit before all of my energy and capability is swallowed up.
With graceful ballet runs, we leave the stage and return to the dressing room. How
was it over so quickly?

45 I remove my make-up and take off my white
clothes. My hair is brushed out and my face returns
to its normal colour. I sip oxtail soup out of a plastic
cup from the vending machine and listen to the
girls around me giggling, shrieking and bubbling
50 over with excitement and excess energy. I feel
exhausted and my toes throb; but I feel immense
relief and such a huge sense of achievement. I
cannot wait to see Mum and Dad and to see what
they thought, although I know that they will be
55 proud of me. I finish my soup and toss the empty
cup into the bin. I check that I have everything
with me and glance once more around the room.
Now I know what the next performance will be like.
Maybe next year I will be the big girl too keen to get
60 on the stage.

Answer the following questions. Underline the correct letter.

1 What does the title mean?

   a being scared of ballet

   b being scared of dancing on stage

   c being scared of being watched

   d being scared of not knowing what to expect

   e being scared of the future

2 Why is her skin referred to as 'deathly white' (line 7)?

   a She is so scared.

   b She is a pale-faced girl.

   c She feels like death.

   d She has heavy make-up on.

   e Her face is not at all shiny.

3 Why does she 'look like a ghost' (line 11–12)?

    a She is dressed totally in white.

    b She is wearing a leotard and tutu.

    c She is scared and ghost-like.

    d She feels as though she is dead.

    e She looks invisible.

4 Why does she want someone who can 'get me out and save me' (line 34)?

    a She hates dancing.

    b She feels sick with nerves.

    c She is scared of forgetting her dance.

    d She might be coming down with a virus.

    e She is too tired to carry on.

5 What do you think the 'magical' happening is (line 39)?

    a She gets saved.

    b She stops feeling sick.

    c The dance is over.

    d She dances forgetting that she is on the stage.

    e She remembers her steps.

6 Why doesn't she join in with the giggling girls in the last paragraph?

    a She has no friends.

    b This is her first show.

    c She is too young.

    d She feels too nervous.

    e She is too tired.

7 What do these words mean as used in the fourth paragraph? Underline the answer.

    a shoved   shovelled / tugged / pulled / hit / pushed

    b mechanical   automatic / frightened / fearful / worried / nervous

    c grimace   fear / frown / smirk / twitch / giggle

    d climax   peak / loudness / end / beginning / middle

    e graceful   fast / slow / smooth / lolloping / jerky

8 What word is used in the text to mean the following? Underline the answer.

1 C

   a to walk in little steps   rush / shuffle / leap / run / bow

   b feeling sick   nauseous / nerves / desperation / push / throb

   c jumpy or edgy   faint / grimace / clammy / panicky / keen

   d lightheaded and dizzy   bubbling / flows / sticky / faint / shake

   e too much   immense / excess / exhausted / keen / jerk

   5

9 What do you think is meant by the **phrase** 'immense relief and such a huge sense of achievement' (line 51–2)?

1 B

   a She is glad that it is all over as she has not let anyone down.

   b She is glad that it is all over as she hated every minute of it.

   c She is glad that it is all over as she loved every second of it.

   d She is glad that it is all over and she has won an award to be proud of.

   e She is glad that it is all over and she is proud of conquering her fear.

   1

10 What effect does the author create in paragraph four with the line that begins 'I jump, I glide…' (line 39–40)?

1 F

   a It shows how she comes alive with the physical actions of dancing.

   b It shows how she thinks about the emotional act of dancing.

   c It shows a list of her range of movements.

   d It shows how she is sadly reduced to nothing more than basic actions.

   e It shows how she repeats the same movements over and over again.

   1

11 How does the author show us that the girl is frightened? Find five words or short **phrases** to support your answer.

1 A

_____

_____

_____

_____

_____

   5

12 Find four pieces of evidence to show that the girl has changed at the end of the story.

1 A

_____

_____

_____

_____

_____

4

Which one word on the right will fit equally well with both pairs of words on the left? Underline the answer.

9 mins

2 E

Example   rhythm, pulse   whip, whisk   dance / cook / <u>beat</u> / belt

13 gasps, wheezes   trousers, slacks   (breathes, jeans, shorts, pants, inhales)

14 shout, yell   weep, lament   (cry, scream, angry, sad, emotional)

15 stage, section   tread, walk   (portion, drama, step, entire, pace)

16 bull, stallion   barge, butt   (push, bump, ram, hit, hog)

17 snap, shatter   holiday, rest   (crack, clash, vacation, stop, break)

5

Underline the one word on the right that has the most similar meaning to the word on the left.

2 C

Example   vision   plotting / smell / <u>sight</u> / style / map

18 cruel   cool / gang / brutal / uncultivated / rude

19 honest   truth / brave / lie / sincere / friendly

20 selfish   considerate / timid / egotistic / dishonest / cheap

21 wicked   cricket / unfriendly / evil / wistful / obsessed

22 quite   silent / softly / fairly / slightly / always

23 seldom   often / never / rarely / always / frequently

24 search   hide / reveal / conceal / forage / scrunch

7

Find the three-letter word that can be added to the capital letters to make a new word. The new word will complete the **sentence** sensibly.

Example   We HED the keys to the estate agent. <u>AND</u>

25 The young child SCBLED all over his brother's homework. _____

26 Liverpool is unusual as the city has a Catholic and Protestant CADRAL.

_____

27 The best schools provide a top class EDUION. _____

28 We had been working so hard, we were in need of a HOAY. _____

29 I crossed the river by the old humpbacked BGE to reach the village. _____

Add the missing letters to the word on the right to make a word with the opposite meaning to the word on the left.

Example   ascended   d <u>e</u> <u>s</u> c <u>e</u> nd <u>e</u> <u>d</u>

30 retire   eme __ __ e

31 restore   ab __ l __ sh

32 refuse   acc __ __ __

33 desirable   u __ att __ __ __ t __ ve

34 deserving   unent __ __ __ ed

35 bravery   cow __ __ d __ ce

6

Some of the words in this paragraph have letters missing. Write out the complete words in the right-hand box, so that the spellings are correct and the paragraph makes sense. The first word has been done for you.

A t __ i __ t __ l __ n is made up of three sports: running, s __ __ __ __ __ ng and cy __ __ __ ng. It is such a challenging event as it tests pers __ __ __ __ __ nce, body strength, physical ability and the mental ability to perform eq __ __ __ ly well in all three sports. There is a need for suppleness, endless __ __ __ rgy and the knack for pacing oneself in addition to the win __ __ __ __ mentality that aims for the top place. Watching people put themselves through such a difficult task is awe-insp __ __ __ __ g.	Eg. triathlon
	36
	37
	38
	39
	40
	41
	42

7

Read the following **sentences** and answer the questions.

Example 'The plane's departure time was 13:45.'
What does the word 'departure' mean? Answer: **b**

a	b	c	d
arriving	<u>leaving</u>	resting	mending

43 'The witness was certain that she had seen an act of aggression.'

   i What does the word 'certain' mean?

a	b	c	d
positive	unsure	curtain	shore

   ii What does the word 'aggression' mean?

a	b	c	d
vileness	violence	viral	virus

44 'The centre of the earthquake caused extreme damage.'

   i What does the word 'centre' mean?

a	**b**	**c**	**d**
perimeter	diameter	radius	core

   ii What does the word 'extreme' mean?

a	**b**	**c**	**d**
safe	expert	considerable	average

45 'He was overwhelmed when he took the prize for academic excellence.'

   i What does the word 'overwhelmed' mean?

a	**b**	**c**	**d**
stunned	bored	relieved	victorious

   ii What does the word 'academic' mean?

a	**b**	**c**	**d**
sporty	intellectual	sensible	behaviour

3

3 H

Rearrange these words to make the longest **sentence** you can.
Underline the word that is **superfluous**.

Example   So cream <u>eat</u> the were cakes delicious.
             The cream cakes were so delicious.

46 Meixiu friends had her a between multiply huge share bag to of sweets.

_____

47 Amber's cat was a jam cake shape in the of birthday.

_____

48 Cook stir-frying is a way to healthier bake.

_____

49 Should we always wash our feet food before preparing our hands.

_____

4

Take a different **conjunction** from the box and place it in a space so that each **sentence** makes sense.

and	as	because	but	if	so	whenever

50 The perfect house was beautifully presented _____ it didn't feel like a home.

51 Sariah never eats meat or fish _____ she is vegetarian.

52 Farooq made all of his friends laugh _____ he told excellent jokes.

53 Padraig passed his 11+ examination _____ he was well-prepared for it.

54 _____ you complete your homework, I think you can go to the football match.

55 Mrs Pious needed to buy half a dozen eggs _____ she caught the bus into town.

56 Butterflies and moths need flowers _____ they can easily be tempted into your garden.

7

Underline the two odd words out in the following groups of words. **9 mins**

Example purple   lilac   <u>olive</u>   <u>sage</u>   violet

57 helicopter	parachute	clouds	stream	pier
58 yacht	canoe	submarine	kayak	galleon
59 July	October	August	February	June
60 prime	squared	cubed	numbers	counting
61 trumpet	violin	cello	trombone	horn

5

Write the **plural** version of the words in these **sentences**.

Example Where are the _cats_? (cat)

62 Our dentists like to see clean _____ (tooth).

63 They have got so many _____ (shelf) full of magazines to read in the waiting room.

64 All of the _____ (child) get a sticker for visiting the dentist.

65 We have to promise not to eat too many _____ (sweet).

66 That way we can avoid lots of _____ (filling)!

5

Read the following **sentences**, underlining the words asked for on the left.

4 C

67 Underline the **preposition**.　　Mrs Hanson slowly plodded around the park.

68 Underline the **conjunction**.　　She hated running, but she wanted to be fitter.

69 Underline the **noun**.　　She would be running her first marathon.

70 Underline the **adjective**.　　She was running to raise funds for a local charity.

71 Underline the **verb**.　　The charity worked with very sick children.

5

Read the following information and then answer the questions that follow.

2 G

72 Sam, Spencer, Lewis and Richard are 10, 12, 14 and 16, but not in that order. Spencer is younger than Lewis and Sam. Richard is younger than Sam but older than Spencer.

How old is Richard? _____

73 Jon and Louisa like fudge and toffee. Paul likes nuts, crisps and toffee. Tina hates toffee and fudge but likes crisps. Louisa likes the same snacks as Paul, Jon likes the same snacks as Tina.

Who enjoys the most snacks? _____

74 Graziano Ricardo came eighth in the race, drawing with five other drivers. There were 24 drivers who began the race, so how many drivers did Graziano beat?

_____

75 Robbie has many apps on his tablet. Joy uses a cookery app when she bakes cakes in the kitchen.

Which statement is true? Underline the answer.

a Robbie has a cookery app on his tablet.

b Joy has a tablet with apps on.

c Joy loves eating cakes.

d Joy loves baking cakes.

e A cookery app can help when baking cakes.

 4

Now go to the Progress Chart to record your score!   Total   90

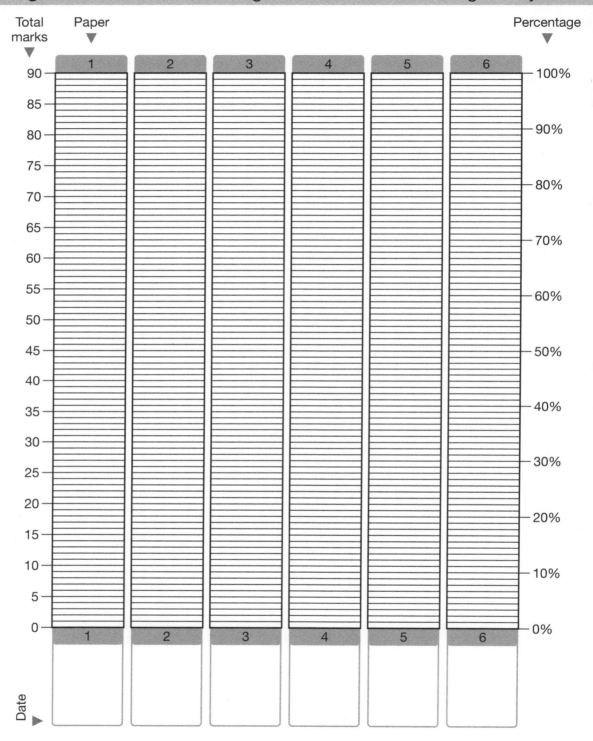

When you've finished the book use the Next Steps Planner